How the Hedgehog got its prickles

By Robin Page · Illustrated by Roger Phillippo

**BIRD'S FARM
BOOKS**

Because the weather was so warm men and women wore no clothes, but they did not look stark naked, as in those dim and distant days men and women were extremely hairy. The hedgehogs wore no clothes either, nor prickles, nor hair. By those who were polite they were known as hairless-hogs, but the rude and impolite called them names such as "baldhogs", "baldilocks" and "nudipigs". Prickles, Spikey and Mrs Tiggy-Winkle were never used, simply because the hedgehog had no prickles.

But most of the fat, worm-fed hogs slept out in the warm prehistoric sun, and they turned brown, a warm prehistoric brown – hedgehog brown as it is known today. They did not burn, as they covered themselves with the juices of sweet-smelling plants – wild mint, wild thyme, wild roses – huge prehistoric wild roses – and wild, sweet-smelling valerian. It protected them from the sun; it was nature's own prehistoric sun-tan lotion. They would put it on, rub it in and dream of worms. In their dreams they would be sniffling for worms, snuffling for worms and eating worms. They never walked in their sleep, or talked in their sleep, but they often dribbled in their sleep – and whenever they woke up they would feel hungry.

The hairless-hogs had many enemies, for wild cats, wild dogs, leopards and lynxes enjoyed eating them.

They loved swimming and on very hot days they would dive, swim under water and blow bubbles just for fun. But while basking on the river bank they had to be careful not to use the sap of valerian as sun-tan oil, for its scent floated many miles through the warm air and attracted potential enemies. Just as modern tame cats enjoy the smell of valerian and roll on the plants in ecstasy, so the wild prehistoric cats loved the smell and rolled on the wild valerian. Sometimes they would become so excited that they would roll on sleeping hairless-hogs by mistake.

Then one day the world began to change. As it became older, so it grew colder, and even the hairless-hogs who preferred the shade came out into the sun. Because it got colder, the worms dug deeper and sniffling for worms and snuffling for worms became so hard, that the hairless-hogs rarely actually ate worms. It got colder and colder. Frost appeared and the backs of the dinosaurs

went white with ice, as the world's first snow storm occurred on the mountains. All the animals wondered, wandered and shivered. Ancient Man put on thick skins to keep warm and went to live in caves; he became the world's first caveman. The hairless-hogs shivered and goose pimples grew. They had no idea why they were called goose pimples; nor had the geese.

They shivered all day long, and all night too
and as it became colder and colder their
goose pimples grew longer and longer.
Sometimes, if the frost came
suddenly, the pimples grew
quickly – long, thin and
pointed, like
miniature icicles.
They looked strange,
they looked funny, but the
hairless-hogs were too
cold to laugh.

If the sun came out, the goose pimples shrank, but if the frost stayed all day long the pimples froze. They became cold and hard and never got smaller. It started to snow on the low ground too.

The mountain hare, the stoat and the polar bear turned white: and there was a rumour that the Ice Age had started. The hairless-hogs had no idea what to do.

They could not sleep flat on the grass, it was too cold. The rabbit holes were filling with snow; the rivers were becoming solid with ice and they had nowhere to hide from their enemies. The wild cats, wild dogs, leopards and lynxes were becoming fat on helpless hairless-hogs and the owls, otters, badgers and buzzards had never lived so well.

The poor hairless-hogs were feeling hungry, but as the ground was so hard with frost they could find no food. However much they sniffled and snuffled and searched for worms, they never found any. It was a desperate time. One day the smallest, weakest,

saddest and coldest hairless-hog, Horace, could stand it no more; he gave up. His goose pimples were so long and pointed that they looked almost like the hedgehog prickles of today. He was crying with cold and curled up into a ball to try to get warm.

Then, all at once his luck changed. The wind blew and he was so weak that he rolled down a leafy bank not yet covered with snow. As he rolled, large fallen leaves were spiked by his long hard goose pimples and he became wrapped in leaves. He rolled and rolled and as he rolled so the layer of spiked leaves grew bigger and bigger until he looked like a great autumn football of fallen leaves.

He came to rest in a hollow; he was dizzy, dozy and upset and too tired to move. He fell asleep and as he slept the wind blew more leaves on top of him, until Horace disappeared completely. The other hairless-hogs were alarmed and shivered and slithered down the bank to look for Horace.

The land became locked in ice and snow. The animals had been right: the Ice Age had set in. Some of the creatures vanished completely because of the cold. The dinosaurs disappeared and the Earth saw them no more; it was as if the world had died.

But gradually and strangely the heat of the sun returned, the snow melted, the ice cracked and the world awoke and became green. It was a new spring and Horace slowly awoke too. He shook the leaves from his goose pimples; he yawned, stretched and felt the warmth of the sun. Prehistoric time had become historic time. The other hairless-hogs emerged from their leaves and they danced with happiness, a long and loud historic dance. They ran and chased and dived into the river.

It was then that they realised something was different. They tried to dive under water for fun, but they could not. They had become prickle-hogs and their prickles kept them bobbing clumsily on the surface like corks.

Although the sun had melted the snow and the ice, the long sharp goose pimples of the hairless-hogs would not disappear – they had become prickles as we know them today, prickles for the whole of historic time.

On the second day of historic time Horace was seen by a hungry wild cat with dinner on its mind, so he ran off in panic towards a small hole in the ground to hide. Again his spikes stopped him – they were too long to let him get into the entrance, and the ferocious wild cat was getting closer. Once more he was desperate, and for the second time in his life he rolled himself into a tight ball.

He was the first ball of prickles the wild cat had ever encountered and soon it was running off howling, its nose feeling like a red-hot pincushion. From that day onwards the prickle-hogs never ran from their enemies, they simply rolled up into a ball of prickles – something they continue to do even now.

Even now in the autumn you can find the prickle-hogs looking for beds of fallen leaves along the hedgerows, and so this is the story of how the hedgehog got its prickles. It tells how the hairless-hog and the prickle-hog became known as the hedgehog too.